Contents

*Levels**	*Title*	*Composer*	*Page*
group A†			
C (T)	**Peas and Carrots**	Doris da Costa	2
C (T)	**The Marvellous Music Box**	Michael Rose	3
C C	**Jumping Jelly Beans**	Sally Adams	4
C (B)	**Free Kick**	Jane Sebba	5
C C C	**Coming! Ready or not!**	Paul Harris	6
C C C	**Fanfare**	Alan Haughton	7
C B (T)	**Bad Hair Day**	Sarah Watts	8
C B (T)	**On Parade**	Doris da Costa	9
C B B	**Lion's Lament**	Jane Sebba	10
group B‡			
C (T)	**I Win, You Win**	Doris da Costa	11
C (T)	**Walk, Don't Run**	Alan Haughton	12
C C	**Who's the Cuckoo?**	Sarah Watts	13
C C	**Year of the Dragon**	Alan Haughton	14
C B	**After You!**	Jonathan Leathwood	15
C C C	**Quick March**	Michael Rose	16
C C B	**Starlight on the Snow**	Robert Hinchliffe	17
C B (T)	**Earth Dance**	David Gordon	18
C B B	**Morning**	Jonathan Leathwood	19

*C = copper; B = bronze; T = teacher; ( ) = the line must be played but cannot be assessed for a Medal.

† *and* ‡ The lines at Copper level are in one of two pitch-groups, to reflect different approaches to note learning at this level. The choice of pitch-group has no bearing on the assessment.

group A (†)

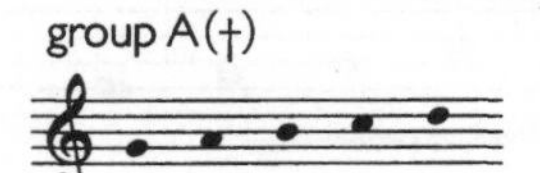

group B (‡)

Peas and Carrots

Doris da Costa

The Marvellous Music Box

Michael Rose

Jumping Jelly Beans

Sally Adams

Free Kick

Jane Sebba

Coming! Ready or not!

Paul Harris

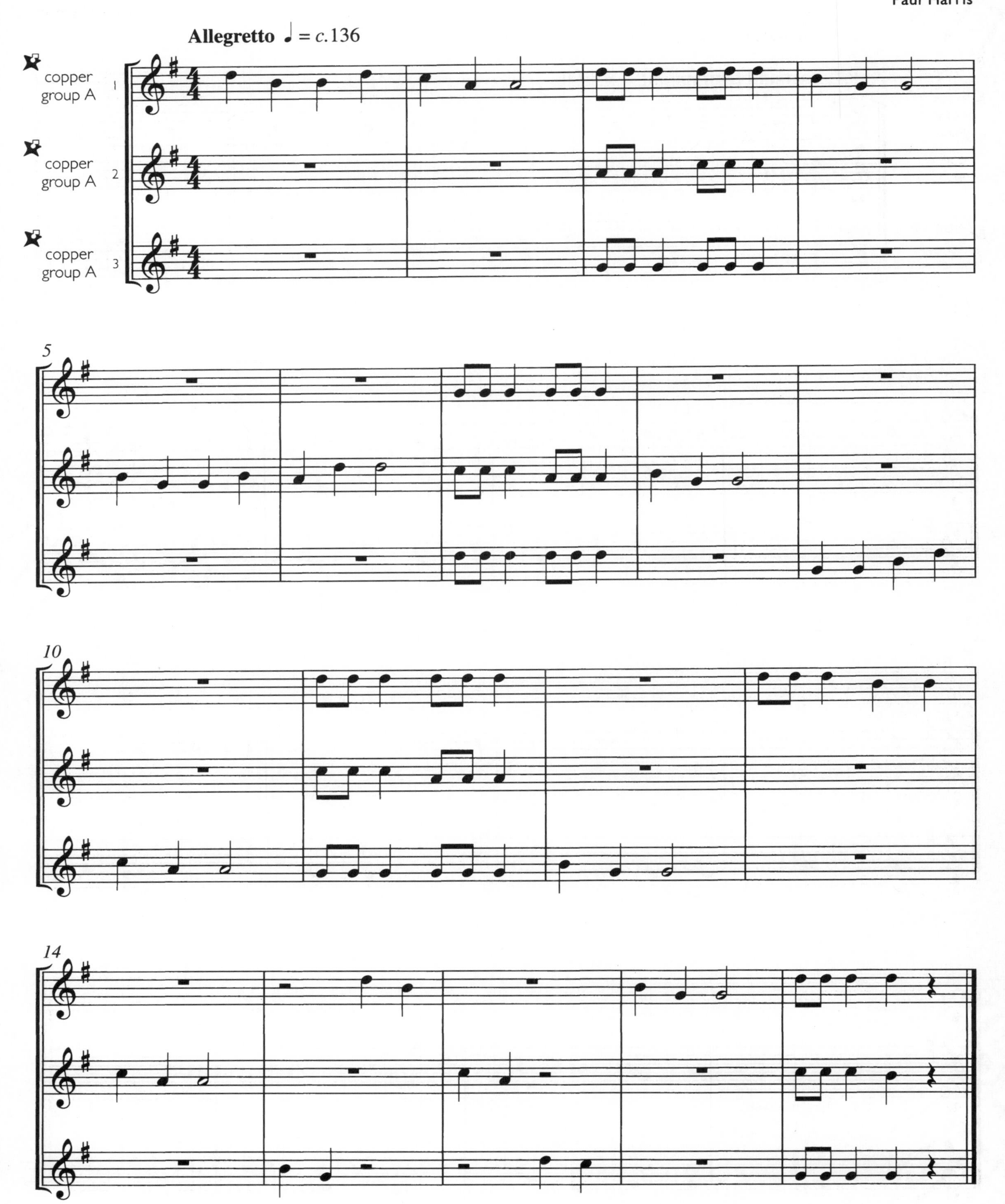

Fanfare

Alan Haughton

Bad Hair Day

Sarah Watts

On Parade

Doris da Costa

Lion's Lament

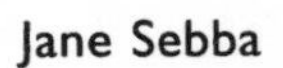

I Win, You Win

Doris da Costa

Walk, Don't Run

Alan Haughton

Who's the Cuckoo?

Sarah Watts

Year of the Dragon

Alan Haughton

After You!

Jonathan Leathwood

Quick March

Michael Rose

Starlight on the Snow

Robert Hinchliffe

Earth Dance

David Gordon

Morning

Jonathan Leathwood